The Willow Pattern

by

Judith Johnson

Resource Material by
Suzy Graham-Adriani
and
Anthony Banks

William Collins' dream of knowledge for all began with the publication of his first book in 1819. A self-educated mill worker, he not only enriched millions of lives, but also founded a flourishing publishing house. Today, staying true to this spirit, Collins books are packed with inspiration, innovation and a practical expertise. They place you at the centre of a world of possibility and give you exactly what you need to explore it.

Collins. Do more.

Published by Collins
An imprint of HarperCollins*Publishers*
77–85 Fulham Palace Road
Hammersmith
London
W6 8JB

Browse the complete Collins catalogue at www.collinseducation.com

© HarperCollins*Publishers* Limited 2005

10 9 8 7 6 5 4

ISBN 000 720 7263

Commissioned by Charlie Evans
Design by JPD
Cover design by Charlotte Wilkinson
Production by Katie Butler
Printed and bound by Martins the Printers

Acknowledgements
Photo credits: p55 photo from All Saints College, (Newcastle) production at the Cottesloe Theatre, July 2004, taken by Simon Annand; p67 The Ronald Grant Archive.

British Library Cataloguing in Publication Data

A Catalogue record for this publication is available from the British Library

Contents

Author's note

In adapting the story of 'The Willow Pattern', I have been inspired by the cult TV series *Monkey*, taken from the ancient Chinese tale of the same name. The acting style of the TV series is larger-than-life caricature, done with tongue in cheek.

The staging of the play that follows is entirely up to each director, although I have made a few suggestions. 'The Willow Pattern' story became known in the West in the late eighteenth century, when the British began to import 'willow' plates from China. Although the story is, of course, uniquely Chinese, I do see it as a universal tale; hence the design of the piece doesn't necessarily need to follow Chinese traditions.

Characters

NARRATOR *Se-rin* — keeps us posted

THE MANDARIN *Eunji* — a very important man

KNOON-SHE *Emma* — his daughter

MIN *Kristy* — her maid and confidante

CHANG *Jiyeon* — the Mandarin's secretary

TA-JIN *Noo* — a possible suitor for Knoon-She

TA-JIN'S MOTHER *Viki* — a wealthy woman

TWO DOVES *Lily + Lisa* — Knoon-She's pets

ENSEMBLE — providing music, dancing, scenery and atmosphere

Chiaoming → lighting → costumes...
Miyuko → sound.

Ciara → singer.

The Willow Pattern

*The **Narrator** explodes, jumps, rolls, runs, glides, skateboards, sky-dives, somersaults or trampolines into the performing space (unless you can think of something even more spectacular). S/he is full of life and eager to tell his/her tale.*

NARRATOR   HOOOOOOOOOOOOOORAAAAAH! HOOPLAAH! AND GREETINGS, MY GOOD FRIENDS!

It is written, 'He that is angry is seldom at ease.' I myself know this to be true. And maybe you know this too. But never has there been a man so ruined by anger as the man whose story I'm about to tell. Long ago, in Ancient Times, long before any of you were born. *(s/he looks around)* Well, most of you anyway. Way way back, when things were different. When things were clearer, when decisions were easier, when life was more definite. And so was death. Back then, there lived a Mandarin.

He was the most important man in the province. He was eminent, influential, powerful. He was the chief, the boss, the main man, the king. He was critical, crucial, focal. Of great consequence, of great magnitude, of great worth. You get the picture. Everyone bowed down before him. Everyone except his daughter.

*There is a loud fanfare or other musical/vocal flourish as the **Narrator** steps back. The **Mandarin**, dressed in fine regalia, enters. He is flanked* *by other dignitaries. He sits on his throne. The dignitaries bow down, then go to the sides of the space. There is another vocal/musical flourish and* **Knoon-She***, dressed up to the nines, is carried on – possibly on a sedan chair – by a retinue of bearers. She is followed on foot by* **Min***.* **Knoon-She** *is placed carefully down and the bearers retreat. Silence.*

MANDARIN	My daughter.
KNOON-SHE	My father.
MANDARIN	I trust you are well.
KNOON-SHE	I am well.
MANDARIN	I trust you are strong?
KNOON-SHE	I am strong.
MANDARIN	You are chaste.
KNOON-SHE	I am chaste.
MANDARIN	You are sweet, you are fragrant.
KNOON-SHE	I am both.
MANDARIN	You are polite?
KNOON-SHE	I am. Thank you so much for asking.
MANDARIN	You are respectful?
KNOON-SHE	Indeed sir, I am.
MANDARIN	You are dutiful?
KNOON-SHE	If that is what you want of me.
MANDARIN	You are loyal.
KNOON-SHE	Most loyal and true.

Beat

MANDARIN   *(smiles)* Then all is well!

*The dignitaries and bearers all smile and sigh happily. **Knoon-She** beams at everyone. **Min** rolls her eyes. The **Mandarin** abruptly stops smiling.*

                (suddenly cross) Come on. Chop chop. What
                are you waiting for? You may all leave now!

*The dignitaries and bearers bow and leave immediately, leaving **Knoon-She**, **Min** and the **Mandarin** alone. There is moment's pause in which the **Mandarin** and **Knoon-She** stare solemnly at each other, then the **Mandarin** breaks into a big grin.*

MANDARIN   My little apple dumpling.

KNOON-SHE   Daddy!

*They run at each other. The **Mandarin** picks **Knoon-She** up and spins her round. She giggles uncontrollably. **Min** shakes her head. They spin faster and faster, then fall down. **Knoon-She** gets up laughing but the **Mandarin** lies on the floor holding his head. **Knoon-She** realises something is wrong and stops laughing.*

MANDARIN   Oh!

KNOON-SHE   Daddy? Are you all right? Min!

MIN   Yes, miss?

KNOON-SHE   Daddy's fallen!

MIN   I expect he was rather dizzy.

KNOON-SHE   Well, don't just stand there, help him up!

*Min gives **Knoon-She** a look, saunters over to where the **Mandarin** is sitting, holding his head. Without looking at him she offers him her hand, which he takes. She pulls him to his feet with rather too much* *force, then goes back to where she was standing. This is all done with a deadpan attitude.*

KNOON-SHE   Daddy, are you all right now?

MANDARIN   I'm fine, pumpkin.

KNOON-SHE   Good, because you haven't given me a present yet today.

MANDARIN   Ah!

KNOON-SHE   *(wheedling)* I was wondering if you really loved me.

MANDARIN   Of course I love you, my precious. You are the most beloved, cherished item – I mean person in my life.

KNOON-SHE   Oh goody, what have you got me?

MANDARIN   See if you can guess.

KNOON-SHE   Is it a fine dress of the best silk in my favourite colours?

MANDARIN   No. For what dress would make you any prettier?

KNOON-SHE   Is it a box of the most delicious hand-made chocolate delights?

MANDARIN   No. You are quite delicious enough already, my angel.

MIN   *(aside)* Is it a bowl in which to be sick?

KNOON-SHE   Is it... a new storybook? Oh please say yes, I want a new storybook more than anything in the world.

MANDARIN   *(worried)* Oh.

MIN   It's not a new storybook.

MANDARIN	It's better! A living thing…
KNOON-SHE	A living thing?
MIN	Two living things!

*He claps his hands and the two doves fly in (or are brought in). These could be puppets, or people, or projections, or anything else you can think of. They fly round the space. Beautifully graceful. Then come to alight on **Knoon-She's** shoulders, or arms, or hold her hands, or in some other way attach themselves fondly to her.*

KNOON-SHE	Oh Daddy! Daddy! They're beautiful!
MANDARIN	I knew you would like them!
KNOON-SHE	*(kissing her father)* You're the best daddy in the whole wide world. Isn't he, Min?
MIN	*(sarcastic)* Oh yeah. The best.
MANDARIN	They will bless your life with the gift of peace.
KNOON-SHE	How wonderful!
MANDARIN	They were your mother's favourite bird.

*The **Mandarin** looks sad. **Knoon-She** goes to him and puts her arms round him.*

KNOON-SHE	Thank you so very much, Daddy. Mummy would have been proud of you.
MANDARIN	She would have been prouder of you.
KNOON-SHE	I love you so much.
MANDARIN	And I you, my sweet sugarplum.

***Min** mimes putting her fingers down her throat. **Knoon-She** and the **Mandarin** part.*

10

MANDARIN	Ah, but I must leave you. Duty calls.
KNOON-SHE	Are you collecting taxes today, Daddy?
MANDARIN	No.
KNOON-SHE	Admonishing peasants?
MANDARIN	No. Writing letters with Chang. Have you seen him today?
KNOON-SHE	*(acting a bit shifty)* Who? Chang? No. I hardly ever see him.
MANDARIN	If you do see him, tell him I'm ready to start. I'll see you later, pumpkin. Enjoy your doves!
KNOON-SHE	I will.

*The **Mandarin** exits. **Knoon-She** stays on-stage, playing with her doves. **Min** exits, but comes back on during the following with a basket of beautiful cloth, which she hangs up on a washing line during the **Narrator's** speech and the next scene. The **Narrator** bounds forwards.*

NARRATOR It is said, 'A friend is one who knows everything about you, and yet still likes you.' Oh so true. And lucky Knoon-She had such a friend. Living in her father's palace was not easy for a spirited young girl like her. She had been without playmates all her life – imagine that. Only her old maid Min to keep her company, and she was hardly a barrel of laughs.

*Min gives the **Narrator** a dirty look. The **Narrator** sticks out her/his tongue at her.*

A girl like this – *(indicating **Knoon-She**)* – a girl full of life. A girl full of vivacity and energy, full of excitement. A girl with verve, with vitality, with vigour.

MIN	Get on with it.
NARRATOR	*(louder, at **Min**)* A girl with dash, dynamism, daring. Such a girl needs a friend to soothe her soul, to calm her thoughts, to temper her flights of fancy.
MIN	Anything in it for the friend?
NARRATOR	Such a friend was Chang. The Mandarin's secretary. A gentle, poetic soul, who loved the very ground that Knoon-She walked upon. It is written: 'Love is patient, love is kind. It does not envy, it does not boast, it is not proud.' The love that Chang had for Knoon-She was just like this. And Knoon-She, despite her headstrong ways, was wise enough to know when she was on to a good thing.

*Enter **Chang**, carrying parchment and quills for writing. The **Narrator** steps back.*

KNOON-SHE	Chang! Look! Look at my doves!
CHANG	They're beautiful, Knoon-She!
KNOON-SHE	Daddy got them for me.
CHANG	I know. He had me write to every menagerie in the province in search of the perfect pair.
KNOON-SHE	Really? Then it is you who chose them for me! Thank you, Chang!

*She throws her arms round him and kisses him. **Min** steps forward, warningly. **Chang** disentangles himself, reluctantly.*

CHANG	Be careful, your father might see us.

Knoon-She *makes a face at **Min** and moves away. Beat.*

12

CHANG	They... stay together all their lives. The doves.
KNOON-SHE	Really?
CHANG	Yes. They are lifelong, devoted partners.
KNOON-SHE	How romantic!
MIN	Do they poo as much as other pigeons?
CHANG	I am sure they'll keep away from your washing, Min.
MIN	They'd better. I'm rather partial to pigeon pie.
KNOON-SHE	*(to the doves)* Don't you listen to her, mean old thing.

*The doves fly to **Min** and alight on her shoulders, or otherwise attach themselves fondly to her.*

MIN	Bog off, before I bite your heads off.

*The doves fly back sharpish to **Knoon-She**.*

KNOON-SHE	I have a gift for you, too.
MIN	Knoon-She!
KNOON-SHE	It's just a little thing!

*She takes a bead out of her pocket. Gives it to **Chang**, who takes it, hesitantly.*

KNOON-SHE	It's my lucky bead. My mum gave it to me when I was really little.
CHANG	Your mother? I can't take this!
MIN	You can't give him Cressida's bead!

KNOON-SHE	I want him to have it! *(to Chang)* You are always so kind to me.

She folds it in his hand, lingering a bit over the hand-holding. **Min** *doesn't see.* **Chang** *moves away nervously.*

CHANG	I... have a new poem for you, Knoon-She.
KNOON-SHE	Oh. No story yet?
CHANG	No, I haven't had time for the story. Your father has been keeping me very busy of late.
KNOON-SHE	*(disappointed)* Oh. You know I love stories!
CHANG	But I do have the poem. They really don't take that long at all.
KNOON-SHE	It is written, 'Poetry is something that heals oneself.'
CHANG	It certainly makes me feel better.
KNOON-SHE	Read it to me and I'll tell you if it makes me feel better too.
CHANG	Okay.

Knoon-She *lies down with her eyes closed.* **Chang** *unrolls one of his parchments. He clears his throat.*

	(for **Min's** *benefit)* It's the kind of poem that a lover would write to his sweetheart. If he had one. It's just an example.
MIN	*(knowingly)* Really.

Chang *coughs, then reads.*

CHANG	When I awake my ears are open,

Listening for you.
My heart is here. My soul is yours.
My love is strong and true.
While I sleep, my eyes are closed,
Dreaming dreams of you.
My arms are waiting. Anticipating.
Are you dreaming too?

Chang looks to **Knoon-She** *for reaction.* **Knoon-She** *lies still with her eyes closed, smiling.* **Min** *stares at* **Chang** *in disbelief. Beat.*

MIN	It is written, 'He who wears his heart on his sleeve often looks stupid.'

Knoon-She sits up.

KNOON-SHE	*(to Chang, fondly)* You're such an old softy.
CHANG	*(embarrassed)* I know.
KNOON-SHE	Come and sit with me.

Chang does so. **Knoon-She** *puts her arms round him. He removes them immediately.* **Knoon-She** *pouts.*

KNOON-SHE	You shouldn't worry about Daddy. You know I can wrap him round my little finger.
CHANG	If he ever thought that we...
KNOON-SHE	That we what?
CHANG	That there was anything... wrong.
KNOON-SHE	Nothing is 'wrong'.
CHANG	I would lose my job.

MIN	He'd chop your arms off if he thought you'd even touched her.
CHANG	Not just my arms.
MIN	It would depend what you had touched her with.

Pause. They all look unhappy. Especially **Chang**.

KNOON-SHE	*(to Chang)* Anyway. When I'm old enough to do what I want, we'll have a house of our own, won't we?
CHANG	It would be lovely if we did.
KNOON-SHE	With a willow tree to watch over us.
CHANG	And a veranda and a swinging seat, where we can both sit and watch the world go by.
KNOON-SHE	Like two doves in a dovecote.
CHANG	Like two doves in a dovecote.

Pause. **Chang** *and* **Knoon-She** *sit. They smile at each other, very fondly. The doves hover contentedly nearby.* **Min** *shakes her head.* **Chang** *sighs.*

CHANG	You'd better go. Your father will be coming. More letters demanding taxes.
KNOON-SHE	He says you're ever so good at them.
CHANG	I'd rather finish your story.
KNOON-SHE	Tell me a little of what it's about before you go!
CHANG	Well...
KNOON-SHE	Please!

CHANG	It's about a girl who lives all alone in a castle, with no friends, who is very unhappy – until one day she is visited by a kind and handsome poet...
MIN	Purrlease!
KNOON-SHE	*(going off)* I'll see you later, Chang.
CHANG	See you later, Knoon-She.

Short burst of music. **Knoon-She**, **Min** *and the doves exit.* **Chang** *sits down with his pen and parchment, poised to write. The* **Mandarin** *enters, through the beautiful cloths. He paces.*

MANDARIN	Dear Land Owner –
CHANG	*(writing)* Dear Land Owner –
MANDARIN	You haven't paid me for some time.
CHANG	You haven't paid me for some time.
MANDARIN	Pay me by Saturday or I will have your head chopped off.

Chang *frowns. The* **Mandarin** *stops pacing.*

MANDARIN	What's the problem?
CHANG	Mm. May I make a suggestion?
MANDARIN	Yes, yes. Go on.
CHANG	I think the Land Owner may run away if you threaten to chop off his head.
MANDARIN	Then I'll have him caught, and when he's caught it won't be just his head that I chop off.

17

Chang flinches.

CHANG	But... the last five Land Owners that we wrote this letter to ran away and were not caught.
MANDARIN	Mm. I'll boil their eyeballs if we ever do catch them.
CHANG	How about a bit of gentle persuasion.
MANDARIN	'Dear Land Owner, please pay me by Saturday or I'll pull out your finger nails?'
CHANG	Well...
MANDARIN	That's not so bad.
CHANG	I was thinking more along the lines of 'Dear Land Owner, your taxes have now been outstanding for some time. Perhaps you would like to come to the Palace, and we can discuss ways in which you can repay your arrears.'

*Pause. The **Mandarin** looks puzzled.*

MANDARIN	Do you think that would do it?
CHANG	It would perhaps make him feel less threatened.
MANDARIN	Less threatened?
CHANG	In which case he would not run away.
MANDARIN	Mm. *(he still doesn't look very sure)*
CHANG	And you could send a couple of your warriors to fetch him, to make sure he kept his appointment.

MANDARIN	Ah! Yes. And while he was at the Palace I could send more warriors to ransack his home and bring me what he owes me!
CHANG	I didn't exactly mean...
MANDARIN	You are a clever old clerk, Chang. So! 'Dear Land Owner – '
CHANG	*(sighs, writes)* 'Dear Land Owner–'
MANDARIN	And so on.
CHANG	And so on.

Chang writes. The *Mandarin* paces.

MANDARIN	Talking of warriors. We need to make some arrangements.
CHANG	Arrangements?
MANDARIN	Yes. Next week, Ta-Jin, the great warrior, is coming to the Palace. And his mother.
CHANG	Ta-Jin and his mother? I see. And to what do we owe this honour?
MANDARIN	I'm going to present him to Knoon-She, as a possible suitor.

Beat.

CHANG	To Knoon-She?
MANDARIN	Yes. I think it's time we started looking at possible husbands for her, don't you? I'm not getting any younger.
CHANG	But Ta-Jin is stupid. His mum still gets him dressed every day. She still cleans his teeth for him. And wipes his...

MANDARIN	He is said to be stupid, although I'm not sure that's true. People always say things like that, and it's often just envy. I do know he is very strong, and also very rich. His father left his mum fifteen donkeys when he died!
CHANG	But, surely, Knoon-She would be better off with someone more... intelligent. Someone she can talk to. Apparently Ta-Jin's mum does all his talking for him.
MANDARIN	Well, Knoon-She doesn't want someone who can outwit her, does she? *(fondly)* She's just like me, she likes to be in control.
CHANG	But I've heard Ta-Jin's mum is very bossy.
MANDARIN	She needs to be, a widow woman, a big strapping lad like that!

Beat.

CHANG	But Ta-Jin spends all his time just... fighting.
MANDARIN	He's a warrior. It's a noble pastime.
CHANG	But what if he fights with Knoon-She? You know how argumentative she can be.
MANDARIN	She'd make minced meat of him!
CHANG	But...
MANDARIN	Enough butting – it's only an introduction, for goodness' sake, Chang! What is the matter with you? Now, you need to order the food. And dancers, too. And fireworks possibly... What do you think?
CHANG	Fireworks? Just for an introduction?

MANDARIN	Perhaps fireworks is pushing it a bit far. Whatever. I'll leave it to you. But I do want to make a good impression. Ta-Jin's mum does own those fifteen donkeys, and with all these Land Owners running away I'm a little down in the donkey stakes at the moment. Let's give them a good welcome, if nothing else!

*The **Mandarin** waltzes off. **Chang** sits for a moment, looking downcast, then rolls up his parchments and exits. The **Narrator** bounds forward.*

NARRATOR	It is written: 'To get used to something is something terrible.' But that is exactly what Chang had to do. He picked himself up, he dusted himself off, and he started to make the arrangements. He ordered the finest food. Tender pig roasted on open fires. Fish, freshly caught from the fast-flowing rivers. Cheese made from the milk of wild goats, fed on fresh mountain herbs. Honey from the bees who buzzed about the exotic flowers of the Palace gardens. Sweet, newly picked, crisp green vegetables and juicy ripe fruit, tasting of summer. Wine of superlative quality. The veritable nectar. He organised the best musicians in the province to be there and the top singers. Really, he kind of went a little overboard. But then again, it has been said, 'Happiness is like a perfume: we cannot sprinkle it someone else, without a few drops falling on ourselves.'

*During the above, the ensemble (including **Min** and directed by **Chang**) bring on a table and chairs. They cover the table with fine cloth from **Min's** washing line. They lay fine food and wine upon the tables, hand decorations about the place (perhaps from **Min's** washing line), and finally sit at the table and eat. Musicians and singers enter. As the **Narrator** finishes, they begin to play and sing. Something pompous,* *celebratory. As they do so the **Mandarin** and a sulky-looking **Knoon-She**, accompanied by **Ta-Jin** and his **mother**, enter. **Ta-Jin** is puffed up and arrogant-looking, his mother haughty and smug. Everyone stands up to bow to the two families, they bow down to each other, then everyone sits and eats. The song ends. The **Mandarin** stand up, with a goblet of wine in his hand.*

MANDARIN   I would like to say a few words of welcome to Ta-Jin and his charming mother. What an honour it is to have such esteemed and wealthy, I mean healthy, visitors. I propose a toast: To Ta-Jin and family!

*He raises his glass. The ensemble repeat: 'To Ta-Jin and family.' Everyone knocks back their wine. **Ta-Jin's Mother** gets to her feet.*

TA-JIN'S MOTHER   Too kind, too kind. I would also like to say a few words. You have been the soul of hospitality, the food has been excellent, the entertainment top-notch and the company – *(she glances at **Knoon-She**)* – very interesting. We would like to offer you some small gifts, to show our appreciation.

*She claps her hands and a donkey is brought on. The **Mandarin** looks absolutely delighted.*

MIN   That small?

MANDARIN   Oh! How absolutely wonderful. Isn't it wonderful, Knoon-She?

KNOON-SHE   *(monotone)* Yeah. Really wonderful.

TA-JIN'S MOTHER   *(prompting Ta-Jin)* And a little something for your beautiful daughter?

*Ta-Jin looks puzzled for a moment. His **mum** nods towards the table. Ta-Jin clicks. He leans under the table, pokes around underneath it for a while, then brings out a very ornate box, overflowing with jewels.*

                    *(To **Knoon-She**)* For you.

Knoon-She takes the box. She is actually impressed, despite herself, but tries to be nonchalant.

KNOON-SHE   Oh. Right. Ta.

Ta-Jin leans towards his mum and whispers something coyly in her ear.

TA-JIN'S MOTHER And now, my son would like to show you his form.

Beat.

MANDARIN   Pardon?

TA-JIN'S MOTHER His form. His movements of his art. The art of fighting.

MANDARIN   Oh! Right! Marvellous. Do go ahead.

*Ta-Jin gets up from the table, moves solemnly into the space in front of the table, and goes through a collection of martial-arts-like movements, which involve use of a fighting stick or sword. He is very serious and very self-important. There is utter silence, and in some quarters disbelief, as they watch. At the end, he bows smugly to **Knoon-She** in the absolute conviction that she thinks he's great. She looks at him, aghast. A beat, then **Ta-Jin's Mother** starts to applaud. The **Mandarin** joins in and everyone else follows politely. **Ta-Jin** milks the applause.*

TA-JIN'S MOTHER *(proudly)* He's been practising in his bedroom.

MANDARIN   I'm sure he has. So. Ta-Jin. You have fought many battles.

*Ta-Jin goes to speak but his **mum** butts in.*

TA-JIN'S MOTHER Oh yes.

MANDARIN And won many victories?

TA-JIN'S MOTHER *(butting in again)* Yes indeed. He's very good.

MANDARIN *(pointedly to **Ta-Jin**)* And tell me, do you, in your spare time, have any hobbies?

TA-JIN'S MOTHER Oh yes, he does.

MANDARIN And what may they be?

TA-JIN'S MOTHER Fighting.

Beat.

MANDARIN Fighting?

TA-JIN'S MOTHER Oh yes. Sparring. Practising moves. Perfecting his form.

MANDARIN *(to **Ta-Jin**)* Anything else?

*Ta-Jin goes to speak again but his **mother** butts in.*

TA-JIN'S MOTHER Oh yes.

MANDARIN Good! And what might that be?

TA-JIN'S MOTHER Training.

MANDARIN I see.

TA-JIN'S MOTHER Building muscles. Improving strength. Ready for the fight.

MANDARIN Right.

TA-JIN'S MOTHER Always. Ready for the fight!

*Ta-Jin flexes his muscles and smiles enticingly at **Knoon-She**. She looks away, astonished. A moment's awkward silence.*

MANDARIN Er, Knoon-She, do you have anything you'd like to ask Ta-Jin?

*Everyone looks at **Knoon-She**.*

KNOON-SHE *(incredulous)* Me?

MANDARIN Yes. Any questions? Any conversation?

KNOON-SHE No!

*Beat. Very awkward pause. After a moment **Ta-Jin** takes a breath and looks as if he's about to say something. Everyone looks at him expectantly. He lets the breath out and looks worried. More awkward silence. **Chang** stands up.*

CHANG Perhaps we should repair to the gardens? We have some beautiful rhododendrons growing near the stream.

MANDARIN Ah yes, the rhododendrons!

TA-JIN'S MOTHER *(getting up)* Rhododendrons, how lovely!

*She takes the **Mandarin's** arm. The party exits, taking the food and table with them, chatting. **Chang** brings up the rear. **Knoon-She**, with **Min**, lingers until last. She grabs **Chang's** hand.*

KNOON-SHE *(lowering voice, mimicking **Ta-Jin's Mother**)* 'Always. Ready for the fight.' I could never marry him!

Chang laughs, pulls his hand away.

MIN	Knoon-She, your guests are waiting. Come on!

Knoon-She kisses Chang quickly on the cheek and exits, with Min. Chang holds his cheek for a moment, happy, then exits, too. Music. The ensemble transform the space into a beautiful palace garden, with a stream running through it. The Narrator dances among the flowers and then speaks.

NARRATOR	It goes without saying, Knoon-She said 'No' to Ta-Jin. Her heart was elsewhere, as we know. The Mandarin accepted his daughter's decision – he wasn't too worried, he'd got as donkey out of the deal and you can't say fairer than that! He decided to let things ride for a while. He was in no great hurry to marry his apple dumpling off. And so Chang and Knoon-She were able to continue seeing each other. They basked in each other's companionship when they could. They relaxed. No one disturbed them. Even Min let them be, for she had been young once herself. They started to think that things would stay like that forever. But they were living in cloud cuckoo land. As the saying goes, 'Love, and a cough, cannot be hid.'

The Narrator steps back. Enter Knoon-She, with Chang. Chang is carrying a parchment. He sits down near the stream. Knoon-She sits opposite him, quite close, and stares at him in excited anticipation. Chang opens up the parchment.

CHANG	Ready?
KNOON-SHE	Yes, yes, yes! I can't wait!

Chang coughs.

CHANG	Right. Here we go, then.

Pause. He coughs again.

	Sorry, I'm ready now. Okay.

He takes a deep breath, lets it out.

KNOON-SHE	Come on!
CHANG	I'm just preparing.
KNOON-SHE	Are you nervous?
CHANG	Well...
KNOON-SHE	You are, aren't you! Silly sausage.
CHANG	I've been working on this story for quite a long time. It's always frightening the first time you... share your work.
KNOON-SHE	How many stories have you written?
CHANG	Just this one.
KNOON-SHE	Oh Chang! And it's especially for me!
CHANG	Yes.

Chang gulps. Beat.

KNOON-SHE	How about if I sit over there, with my back to you? So you can't see my face. Just in case it looks like I'm not enjoying it. *(quickly)* Although I'm sure I will.
CHANG	No, no, that's okay. I'd rather know what you really feel. I think.

KNOON-SHE	But what if I don't like it?
CHANG	Then you must tell me.
KNOON-SHE	Right.

*Beat. **Chang** thinks.*

CHANG	Actually, I'd rather you pretended you like it even if you don't, to be honest.
KNOON-SHE	Would you? Wouldn't that be like, lying, though? I don't want there to be any untruths between us, Chang.
CHANG	Then, perhaps if you don't like it, you could find one small thing in it that you did like, and praise me just for that.

*Pause. **Knoon-She** considers this for a moment, then:*

| KNOON-SHE | Yes! That's we'll do. |
| CHANG | Okay! |

Pause.

| KNOON-SHE | Come on then! |

He coughs, then suddenly launches into it, reading very quickly.

	'Many years ago, in ancient times, there lived a girl called Pnoon-Mee.'
KNOON-SHE	Who?
CHANG	Pnoon-Mee.

Knoon-She beams.

KNOON-SHE	Okay!
CHANG	*(still reading very fast)* 'Pnoon-Mee lived all alone with her father in a castle that stood at the very ends of the earth.'
KNOON-SHE	Ends of the what?
CHANG	The earth.
KNOON-SHE	Okay.
CHANG	*(still fast)* 'No one ever came to visit the castle, because Pnoon-Mee's father was said to be a mean and irascible old man who would not welcome visitors into his home.'
KNOON-SHE	Chang?
CHANG	Yes? Is it terrible?
KNOON-SHE	No! But you need to slow down a bit.
CHANG	Right. Slow down. Okay.

He takes another deep breath.

CHANG	'Pnoon-Mee was very lonely. She spent her days staring out across the sea, longing for a ship to sail into view – but none ever came. She spent her nights dreaming of a world where many people lived in harmony together. Where there was music and songs and dancing. Her father didn't like too much noise.'
KNOON-SHE	Poor Pnoon-Mee.
CHANG	Yes.

Pause.

KNOON-SHE	And?
CHANG	And?
KNOON-SHE	What happened next?
CHANG	Do you think the bit about the ship works?
KNOON-SHE	Yes, yes. It's fine. Does the Poet come soon?
CHANG	You don't think it's a little extraneous to the plot?
KNOON-SHE	What? Extraneous? No, yes, whatever...
CHANG	*(stricken)* Yes!
KNOON-SHE	Whatever! Get on with the story.
CHANG	*(worried)* All right.

Chang lifts up the parchment.

CHANG	'One day, when Pnoon-Mee was walking in the gardens of the Castle, she heard a sound she had never heard before in her life. It was the voice of someone else, someone other than herself or her father.'
KNOON-SHE	It was him, wasn't it? The Poet! I knew it!
CHANG	*(a bit cross)* Just a minute.
KNOON-SHE	Was he handsome, was he kind?
CHANG	Just a minute!
KNOON-SHE	Was he tall? Or short?
CHANG	'It was the voice of a Poet...'
KNOON-SHE	I knew it!

30

CHANG	'... who had lost his way and wandered into the Castle gardens by mistake.'
KNOON-SHE	Ooh! Can they keep him secret from her father? Please, Chang, that would make the story more exciting, if they had to hide him somewhere in the Castle!
CHANG	More exciting? Isn't it exciting already?
KNOON-SHE	*(carried away)* No, not quite enough yet, but I think if we added a bit where he had to hide, and her father knew, and he threatened to... to pull her fingernails out unless she told him where the Poet was, that would be brilliant!
CHANG	It would be a bit bloodthirsty.
KNOON-SHE	Yes! It needs a bit of action, don't you think?
CHANG	It's not that kind of story.
KNOON-SHE	Oh, but it would be great... if... it was.

Knoon-She grinds to a halt. Chang is looking very miffed.

KNOON-SHE	What's the matter?
CHANG	This is my story, not yours.
KNOON-SHE	I was just saying.
CHANG	I've been writing it for a long time. It's all worked out. There's no room for a change in the plot now.

Beat.

KNOON-SHE	Sorry.

No answer from **Chang**.

It's ever so good.

Still no answer.

Please don't fall out with me, Chang.

Knoon-She *moves right next to* **Chang**. *She puts her arm round him.*

I got a bit carried away. If the story hadn't been so good in the first place I wouldn't have got so excited.

CHANG	You said it wasn't exciting.
KNOON-SHE	It is. Really.
CHANG	You're not just saying that?
KNOON-SHE	Of course not.

Beat. During the following exchange, **Knoon-She** *and* **Chang** *get closer and closer until they are on the verge of kissing.*

KNOON-SHE	You were really cross with me then.
CHANG	I know.
KNOON-SHE	You've never been cross with me before. It was horrible.
CHANG	I was only a little cross.
KNOON-SHE	Really?
CHANG	Of course. I'm not cross any more.
KNOON-SHE	Give me a kiss, to prove it.
CHANG	I... mustn't! Min isn't far away.

KNOON-SHE	She won't tell.
CHANG	Won't she?
KNOON-SHE	No.

Beat. Silence. They are millimetres from each other.

KNOON-SHE	Are you going to kiss me?
CHANG	Okay.

Chang kisses Knoon-She. Almost immediately, the Mandarin enters.

MANDARIN	What is going on here?
KNOON-SHE	Daddy! How wonderful to see you!

Knoon-She launches herself at the Mandarin, a desperate hug. He pushes her off. Addresses Chang.

MANDARIN	I asked you a question.
KNOON-SHE	I had some dirt in my eye, Daddy. Isn't Chang kind? He was trying to get it out.
MANDARIN	Knoon-She, be quiet.
KNOON-SHE	But...
MANDARIN	*(shouting)* BE QUIET!

Silence. The Mandarin walks over to Chang and pulls him up by his collar.

MANDARIN	I am waiting for an explanation.

Min comes running on.

MIN	Is everything all right, I heard shouting?
KNOON-SHE	Min!
MANDARIN	*(to **Chang**, shouting in his face)* I AM WAITING FOR AN EXPLANATION!
CHANG	I... I was kissing Knoon-She.
MIN	What?
KNOON-SHE	No!
CHANG	She... she didn't ask me to. She hasn't done anything. It was my idea, I couldn't help myself. Your daughter is more beautiful and more dear to me than anyone or anything on this earth.

*Silence. After a moment the **Mandarin** drops **Chang** down.*

KNOON-SHE	*(suddenly, to Chang. Shouting at the top of her voice)* RUNNNNNNNNNNNNNNNNNNN!

__Chang__ gets up, and runs off stage.

MANDARIN	What? Come back! Where's my warriors? Warriors!

*__Knoon-She__ grabs her **father** to stop him going off in search of warriors. He struggles.*

MANDARIN	Get off me! Warriors! Warriors!
KNOON-SHE	No! Let him go!

*During the struggle, **Min** quietly exits after **Chang**. The **Mandarin** and **Knoon-She** don't see her. The **Mandarin** finally breaks free of **Knoon-She**, knocking her to the ground as he does so.*

MANDARIN   *(to **Knoon-She**)* You disgust me.

*He exits. Immediately, some warriors run across the space and go in the direction that **Chang** and **Min** went. There is music or shouting, cacophonous sounds. The ensemble comes on and makes a fence round the garden and round **Knoon-She**. **Knoon-She** watches, horrified, as she is fenced in, then covers her face. During this the **Narrator** steps forward and speaks, while the doves come to join **Knoon-She**, flying round her, trying to comfort her.*

NARRATOR   What sadness! What sorrow and sadness and strain. The Mandarin was so angry with his daughter, he placed a high fence round the Palace and garden, and refused to let her see anyone! He sent out warriors, searching for Chang high and low, promising a reward of four donkeys to anyone who could bring back his dead body. And worst of all, he told Knoon-She he had decided something. He had decided she was to marry Ta-Jin after all. Knoon-She was heartbroken. She wandered the garden day after day, thinking about Chang. She wouldn't admit it to herself, but deep in her heart she felt he was dead.

Knoon-She wanders. The doves follow her.

Not even her old maid Min had been allowed to see her, so there was no one to tell her that Chang had not been found, and no one knew where he was. She was unhappier than she had ever been in her life but, as it is said, 'The soul would have no rainbow if the eyes had no tears.' And then, anyway, one day something happened to wipe her tears away.

*Music: light, hopeful. The **Narrator** steps back. **Knoon-She** sits by the stream. After a moment a small boat floats down it. **Knoon-She** is amazed, she looks around her to check no one is looking, picks up the* *boat. Inside is the bead she gave **Chang** earlier, and the parchment with his story. She holds the bead up to the light then clasps it to her heart. She picks up the story and the boat, then exits, quickly. The fence and gardens exit with her, as do the doves, leaving the space bare. Enter **Chang**, with a sleeping-mat. He puts the sleeping-mat on the floor, then lies on it. He looks sad. After a moment, **Min** enters. She is carrying a bowl of water with a cloth to wash in it. The parchment with the story on it is stuck into the belt behind her back. **Chang** sits up.*

CHANG   Any new from the Palace?

MIN   They still won't let me see her, but apparently it's the same story. The Mandarin is not talking to the daughter. The daughter is not talking to the Mandarin. Both are in a foul frame of mind. No one in the Palace dares speak, let alone smile or laugh.

CHANG   Oh dear.

MIN   Another warrior has returned, finding no trace of you anywhere in the province. They have searched east and west, north and south. They have left no stones unturned. But nobody has thought to look so close. It is as I said. All roads lead you astray. Stay home.

CHANG   You are very kind to keep me here.

MIN   I am an old fool and I will suffer for it.

CHANG   Your tongue is sharp but your heart is soft.

MIN   Your intention is good but your words are twaddle.

CHANG   I only mean to thank you for helping me.

MIN   Then say that. The best poetry is direct.

CHANG   You think so.

MIN	I know so. Direct. And unsentimental.
CHANG	I see.
MIN	I hope you do.

Chang sighs.

CHANG	*(sentimentally)* Is my beloved and most cherished Knoon-She truly unhappy?
MIN	*(shakes her head)* Unbelievable.

Min puts the bowl down and starts washing the cloth.

CHANG	I miss her with all my heart.
MIN	She's feeling a bit better.
CHANG	Is she?
MIN	She got your message.
CHANG	*(jumping to his feet)* You're kidding. The boat?
MIN	Yep, strange as it may seem, the plan worked.
CHANG	Did she return it back down the stream? With the story?
MIN	She... did.

Pause.

CHANG	Well? Do you have it?
MIN	*(stops washing)* I do have it.

Beat.

CHANG	And? So? Can you give it to me?
MIN	I can give it to you, but I have to warn you.
CHANG	Yes?
MIN	She's finished the story.
CHANG	What?
MIN	Try not to be cross. It has a happy ending.

Chang composes himself.

CHANG	The important thing is, she got it, she knows I'm alive.
MIN	*(giving over the parchment)* I hope you feel the same after you've read it.

Chang opens the parchment, sits down and reads. **Min** continues washing.

CHANG	*(after a bit, looking up, astounded)* The Poet is dead!
MIN	Good thing. He took himself far too seriously.
CHANG	But...
MIN	Read on.
CHANG	I thought you said it had a happy ending!
MIN	It does. But there are more surprises first.

Chang reads. **Min** washes.

CHANG	*(looks up)* She's killed the father!

MIN	Yes. The fight was terrific, I thought.
CHANG	But Pnoon-Mee would never have been able to wield an axe like that! Would she?
MIN	Hell hath no fury... And so on.
CHANG	*(reading)* Ah! Wait! The Poet has come back to life!
MIN	Yes. Cunning twist that. Giving him the paralysing powder.

Beat.

CHANG	*(happy)* And now they are married, and the Castle is full of people, 'Living in harmony together. With music and songs and dancing.'
MIN	I told you it was happy.
CHANG	Just like it's going to be for us. A happy ending.
MIN	Don't count your chickens.
CHANG	Min?
MIN	*(suspicious)* Mm?
CHANG	Are you sure I can't creep up to the fence? Catch a glimpse of her in the Palace gardens?
MIN	I'm sure.
CHANG	But I would so love just to see her dear, dear face.
MIN	You would lose your own dear face if someone caught you.
CHANG	But...

MIN	We stick to the plan. It's the only way. 'If we do not change direction, we will probably get to where we are going,' as the saying goes.
CHANG	When is Ta-Jin arriving?
MIN	Next week. There isn't long to wait.
CHANG	So I'm stuck here until then.
MIN	It's not so bad. Without going outside, you may know the whole world.
CHANG	You are a very wise person, Min.
MIN	I have my ignorance to thank for the few things I know.
CHANG	You know you are risking... everything by helping us.
MIN	I promised Knoon-She's mother I would always take care of her, and that is what I am going to do.
CHANG	You are a genuinely good person.
MIN	And when you and Knoon-She set up your house together, far away from here, I will be with you and I will be free.
CHANG	Yes! We will all be free. I really believe we will.

Min finishes washing her cloth. Stands up.

MIN	I don't think we have an ice cream's chance in Hell. But, as the saying goes, 'You have only failed when you have failed to try.'

*Min exits. **Chang** cradles his parchment in his arms. Then rolls up his sleeping mat and exits, too. The **Narrator** steps forward.*

NARRATOR   The week passed faster than anyone could have imagined, and soon it was the eve of Knoon-She and Ta-Jin's nuptials. The Mandarin threw a stag party and invited all the eminent men of the province, such was the local tradition. Knoon-She was cleansed and preened while Ta-Jin and the Mandarin caroused the night away. And, unbeknownst to anyone, Min and Chang set their plan into action..

*Music. Wedding celebrations. The **Mandarin**, **Ta-Jin**, and other men come staggering onto the stage, roaring drunk, singing a drinking song at the tops of their voices. One of these men is **Chang**, in disguise.*

Stag song (just the lyrics – make up your own tune).

1 He's old enough to vote,
He's sowed his wild oats,
He's brought a new coat
For the wedding!

She's got him bewitched
So it's time they was hitched
And lying on their newly stitched
Bedding.

Chorus
Man and wife!
Man and wife!
They're in it for life.
He and she!
He and she!
For e-tern-it-tee.

Boy and girl,
Boy and girl,
Oyster and pearl.
Girl and boy,
Girl and boy,
A bundle of joy.

2 A man's life is short
And he don't need much thought
About how much he needs
A dear spouse.

To keep him indoors
To lay down the law,
To berate him and call him
A louse.

Chorus

Man and wife!
Man and wife!
Oh what a life.

He and she,
He and she,
Take pity on me!
Boy and girl,
Boy and girl,
Oh how she makes me hurl!

Girl and boy,
Girl and boy,
She does cloy and annoy!
Girl and boy,
Girl and boy,
She does cloy and annoy!

As they sing, on the other side of the stage **Knoon-She** *enters, wearing plain undergarments. During what follows, she is dressed up in her* *wedding outfit by two handmaids (not* **Min**). *Her outfit should be very ostentatious and made up of many pieces.* **Knoon-She** *stands very still and looks stoic throughout. The men finish their drunken song and go to sit down.*

MANDARIN   *(his arm round* **Ta-Jin**, *drunk)* So, my boy, soon
                 to be married, eh?

Ta-Jin *nods contentedly.*

                 You and my girl, all done up, all fine and
                 dandy and ready to go!

Ta-Jin *nods.*

                 D'you know, I remember my own wedding.
                 I stood in the Pagoda, awaiting my bride. I'd
                 never seen her before – we didn't in those
                 days – so I was pretty nervous, I can tell you.
                 Then, suddenly, there she was, walking
                 through the arbour towards me. My beautiful
                 Cressida. Her face framed by lotus blossoms. A
                 vision.

Beat. The **Mandarin** *struggles against tears.* **Ta-Jin** *looks suitably sad.*

                 She was a diamond. A diamond of a wife.
                 Kind and sweet and joyful, she always
                 cheered me up, I can tell you. I never was a
                 very happy person.
                 I always had a terrible temper so people
                 tended to keep away from me. But she didn't
                 even seem to notice. Not a cross word
                 between us. Ten years. And then she gave me
                 a wonderful gift.

*Ta-Jin looks questioningly at the **Mandarin**.*

> A daughter. A darling little bundle of
> enchantment. And just as my wife was gentle
> and kind, her daughter was vigorous and
> strong. Like a little firecracker, full of fizz. I
> loved her so much.

Ta-Jin nods happily.

> And now my Cressida is dead and you are
> going to take my apple dumpling away from
> me.

*The **Mandarin** starts to cry. Ta-Jin looks confused.*

> (*crying, patting **Ta-Jin** on the back*) Don't
> worry. It's my fault. I've brought it on myself
> yet again with that stinking temper of mine. It
> has always been my downfall. D'you know,
> when my beloved spouse was taken away
> from me by that damned fever, I went into a
> rage the like of which has not been seen in
> this province before or since. Even I was
> amazed. I threw out all the people who lived
> in the Palace at the time. I kept only a few
> servants. I shouted the house down.
> I broke all the statues. I kept Knoon-She away
> from people, I didn't want her to catch
> something and die too, you see. And that's
> how come she fell in love with that insipid
> secretary of mine instead of a fine healthy
> fellow like yourself. And now I'm making her
> marry someone she despises, and again it's all
> my fault.

*Pause. Ta-Jin looks concerned. He knits his brows. After a moment he
takes a deep breath as if to say something. The **Mandarin** looks at him*

44

expectantly. **Ta-Jin** *lets the breath out. The* **Mandarin** *looks away, but then* **Ta-Jin** *breathes deep and speaks. When his voice comes out it is very thin and weedy (David Beckham springs to mind).*

TA-JIN   Can I say something?

Beat. Everyone stares at **Ta-Jin** *in amazement because he's spoken.*

MANDARIN   Please do!

TA-JIN   If Knoon-She doesn't like me, maybe we
                  shouldn't be getting married at all.

Beat, all stare at him, aghast.

MANDARIN   *(after a moment, heartily)* Nonsense, my boy.
                  We can't call off a good wedding at this late
                  stage. What would we tell the guests? Besides,
                  the ten donkeys your mother gave me have
                  settled in beautifully. We wouldn't want to
                  disturb them, would we? *(The Mandarin leaps
                  to his feet.)* Come along, we can't sit moping
                  on the floor! We have drinking to do, we must
                  make merry, we must party and revel and
                  whoop it up!

The men all jump up and throw themselves into their drunken song once again, this time with a choreographed dance, too. The maids have by now dressed **Knoon-She** *and left. She is sitting alone, staring sadly into space.* **Chang** *quietly slips away from the drunken revelry towards* **Knoon-She**. *As he does so, his hat falls off. He goes to* **Knoon-She**. *She looks confused, wonders who he is. He takes off the rest of his disguise so she can recognise him.* **Knoon-She** *gasps and throws her arms around him.* **Chang** *undresses* **Knoon-She**, *taking off her wedding clothes until she is in her undergarments once more. This should be a tender moment, in contrast to the drunken wedding song going on at the same time. They embrace, then* **Chang** *shushes* **Knoon-She**, *takes her hand.* **Knoon-She** *stops a moment to grab the box of jewels given to her by* **Ta-Jin**, *then* **Chang** *leads her off. As he does so,* **Ta-Jin** *notices* **Chang's** *hat on the* *floor. He looks over to where **Knoon-She** was. He looks puzzled, whispers something in the **Mandarin's** ear. The **Mandarin** looks over to where **Knoon-She** was, looks absolutely livid, then yells at the top of his voice.*

MANDARIN   STOOOPPPPPPPPPPPPPPPP!!

*Everyone stops dancing and singing. Silence. Then the **Mandarin** takes a deep breath and shouts again.*

MANDARIN   BRINNNNNNNNNNNNNNNNNNNNNNNGG GGGGGGGGGG!!

MEEEEEEEEEEEEEEEEEEEEEEEEEEEEEEE EEEEEEEEEEEE!!

MYYYYYYYYYYYYYYYYYYYYYYYYYYYYYYY YYYYYYYY!!

WAAAAAAARRIIIIIORRRRRRRRRS!!

*Everyone exits. Music: loud, cacophonous. The ensemble comes on and makes a bridge. **Min** waits on the other side of the bridge in a boat. After a moment **Knoon-She** and **Chang** come running onto the bridge. They are soon followed by **Ta-Jin**, the **Mandarin** and some warriors. The warriors and **Ta-Jin** have fighting sticks. **Chang** and **Knoon-She** turn to face them. It looks like they've had it, but then **Min** springs forward with fighting sticks for **Chang**, **Knoon-She** and herself. A fierce fight follows which is finally won by **Min**, **Chang** and **Knoon-She** (**Knoon-She** and **Min** proving to be the best fighters). At some point during the fight, **Knoon-She** gives **Chang** the jewellery box to hold so she can fight better. The **Mandarin** notices this. At the end of the fight, the warriors and **Ta-Jin** lie strewn all over the space, while **Chang**, **Knoon-She** and **Min** escape in the boat.*

MANDARIN   *(as the boat draws away)* Do something! Do something! Do something!

*No answer from the exhausted warriors and **Ta-Jin**. The **Mandarin** runs to the end of the bridge and shouts after his daughter.*

I'll find you, d'you hear me! I'll find you. And when I do, you'll be sorry you did this to me!

*The two doves come flying onto the bridge, about to follow **Knoon-She**. The **Mandarin** grabs them. They struggle but he holds them tight and exits with them. Music stops. The warriors and **Ta-Jin** get slowly to their feet, nursing their wounds, and leave the space. After a moment, the **Narrator** bounds forward.*

NARRATOR   Phew! Phewee, gadzooks and gosh! What a kerfuffle, what a to-do. What a turn up for the books. Knoon-She and Chang sailed away until they found a small island, protected by a beautiful willow tree.

*The bridge breaks up and exits, leaving a few people behind to represent or make the willow tree. As the **Narrator** speaks, **Knoon-She**, **Chang** and **Min** enter. They start to build two houses. One for **Knoon-She** and **Chang**, one for **Min**. This can be done using the ensemble, or blocks, or whatever you like. The houses are simple but elegant. There is s swing seat at the front of **Knoon-She** and **Chang's**, which they sit on when the building is finished.*

And here they made homes for themselves, and for Min, too, because, as it is written, 'You can get everything you want in life if you help enough people get what they want.'

Min puts her thumb up and smiles.

The lovers and their friends were happy. They were contented, blissful, pleased. They were jovial, delighted, cheery and glad.

MIN   Enough.

NARRATOR	They were like doves in a dovecote. They were on Cloud Nine.
MIN	Enough!
NARRATOR	Back home, in the province they had left behind, it was a different story. The Mandarin went on the rampage, breaking up the Palace and chucking out all his wedding guests. It was like when his wife died, only worse. Ta-Jin and his mum took back all their donkeys and left the place in a huff. And the Mandarin, alone in his Palace with no one to talk to, became more and more vengeful.

Enter the **Mandarin***, looking wild and angry. He brings with him the two doves, in a cage.*

Knoon-She *and* **Min's** *houses remain on-stage.*

It is said, 'Those who think of revenge keep their wounds open.' Oh, so true. The Mandarin could not get past it. All he could think about was the way his beloved Knoon-She had betrayed him. He wanted to find his daughter and Chang and have them thrown into prison. But by the law of the province he could not do so because, actually, they hadn't really done anything wrong. By now they were both of age, they could marry whoever they liked. It was only tradition that saw the matter differently. Tradition, and the Mandarin. He was livid but his hands were tied. So he brooded and brooded and fretted and festered until, one day, he had a visitor.

Enter **Ta-Jin's Mother***.* **Narrator** *steps back. The* **Mandarin** *jumps up, shocked.* **Ta-Jin's Mother** *bows to him, briefly.*

TA-JIN'S MOTHER   Mandarin.

MANDARIN   Madam.

TA-JIN'S MOTHER   Are you all right? You look a little...
                  dishevelled.

MANDARIN   I... haven't been feeling too good.

TA-JIN'S MOTHER   Yes, well, I suppose that's understandable. You
                  have been made a mockery of. The whole
                  province is talking about you – how foolish
                  you looked, betrayed by your own daughter.
                  You know she's living out of wedlock with
                  that scribe, don't you? She was obviously bad
                  from the start. Thank goodness my Taji didn't
                  get to marry her.

MANDARIN   Can I help you with anything or are you just
                  here to exercise your mouth?

TA-JIN'S MOTHER   *(pursing her lips)* The small matter of the
                  jewellery box.

MANDARIN   The what?

TA-JIN'S MOTHER   The box of jewels given to your daughter, by
                  my son, as an introduction present. We want
                  it back.

*The **Mandarin** looks puzzled.*

MANDARIN   I don't remember any jewellery box!

TA-JIN'S MOTHER   Mandarin! Aren't you ashamed enough? Do
                  not disgrace yourself further by lying now!

MANDARIN   How dare you accuse me of lying! I may be a
                  fool, yes. I may be disgraced. I may be a silly,
                  bad-tempered, irascible, surly old man but...

49

He grinds to a halt.

                        ... just a minute! Was it blue?

TA-JIN'S MOTHER What?

MANDARIN The box, woman, was it blue?

TA-JIN'S MOTHER Yes, I think it was, but...

MANDARIN *(over the moon)* I saw it in his hands the night they went away! Theft! Theft!

TA-JIN'S MOTHER What are you going on about?

MANDARIN *(jubilant)* Madam, I am very sorry to have to tell you, your jewellery box has been stolen!

TA-JIN'S MOTHER Has it?

MANDARIN Yes, by my erstwhile secretary, Chang. But don't you worry, I will do my utmost, believe me, to bring it, and the thief, and his accomplices, right back where they came from.

TA-JIN'S MOTHER And how are you going to do that? No one knows where they are.

MANDARIN *(eyeing the doves, who flutter and beat their wings against the cage)* Oh, I think I know someone who could find them.

He goes over to the doves and opens the doors to the cage. The doves flutter and then fly out.

MANDARIN *(taking **Ta-Jin's Mother's** hand)* Don't worry, madam. You will have your jewellery box. And I will have my revenge.

*The doves fly off, the **Mandarin** follows. **Ta-Jin's Mother**, looking* *confused, exits the other way. The* **Narrator** *springs forward. During the following, the doves fly round the hall and through the audience, followed by an intensely resolute* **Mandarin**. *Eventually they come back up into the performing space to where* **Knoon-She**, **Chang** *and* **Min** *have their houses.*

NARRATOR   *(urgently)* Vengeance. Retribution. Reprisal. Retaliation. Reckoning. Justice. Punishment. Comeback. The words ran round the Mandarin's head as he followed Knoon-She's doves closer and closer to his daughter. When a man grows angry, his reason rides out. When wrath speaks, wisdom veils her face. When temper rises, reason drops. Night fell and the Mandarin got nearer.

Knoon-She *and* **Chang** *snuggle down to sleep in their houses.* **Min** *does the same.*

And as he got nearer, his rage grew bigger, until he had forgotten all about the jewellery box and he had forgotten all about throwing Chang in prison. All he could see was a big red mist, and he just wanted to envelop them in it so they could feel exactly just how hurt, how hurt and full of rage he was.

Silence. The doves have arrived at the houses. They hover around and watch the sleeping **Knoon-She** *and* **Chang**. *The* **Mandarin** *creeps over. The doves fly away in distress. The* **Mandarin** *stares in at his sleeping daughter and* **Chang**. *He is breathing very heavily, seething. Suddenly, he runs off. The doves come back and start beating their wings against the house but* **Chang** *and* **Knoon-She** *don't wake up. The* **Mandarin** *runs back on with a flaming torch and throws it into the house. The house begins to burn. The* **Mandarin** *hides at the side and watches.* **Knoon-She** *and* **Chang** *wake up. They scream, cry for help and try to get out of the house, but they are trapped.* **Min** *wakes up and tries to help them out, tries to put out the fire, but she can't. the doves flap about in distress. Finally the house is razed to the ground and* **Knoon-She** *and* **Chang** *lie dead on the* *floor. The doves settle beside their bodies.* **Min** *falls to her knees and sobs. The* **Mandarin** *stands up, in shock. He looks terrible. He takes two steps forward, then lets out a cry of anguish.*

MANDARIN   Nooooooo!

The **Mandarin** *runs off. The* **Narrator** *steps forward.*

NARRATOR   It was a very sad time for the people of the
                 province.

The **Ensemble** *enters. Music or song: sad, mournful. All gather round the bodies of* **Knoon-She** *and* **Chang***, as though at a funeral.*

                 The Mandarin, a broken man, disappeared.
                 The rumour was he had become a hermit.
                 Living alone in a cave on the mountain,
                 forever regretting and full of remorse.

The two **doves** *slowly begin to twitch and come to life.*

                 And that is my story. The moral is clear. They
                 say anger is a fear of losing control. I say lose
                 your fear. Control ain't everything it's cracked
                 up to be.

The funeral song/music is repeated.

End.

Staging the play

THE SET

The Willow Pattern could be performed in almost any large space, for instance in your school hall or a large classroom. You may like to be more adventurous, however, and stage it in the open-air in a playground, on a field or as a promenade in the school grounds, with the audience following the performers around on foot. As there is a lot of action in the play and there is potential for the Chorus to make lots of movement, you will probably want to use as large an acting area as you can. You might decide to stage it in an end-on arrangement, in thrust or in-the-round. Whichever you choose, the performing space should remain as uncluttered as possible throughout, allowing the maximum amount of free movement and enabling the audience's focus to be on the actors.

Most of the action takes place outdoors. If you are in an end-on or thrust format you may choose a simple skycloth in a neutral colour to cover the back wall. If you are performing in-the-round, the floor of the acting area could be a bright off-white that will lift the energy of the performers and give the impression of a hot summer's day, which is when most of the story takes place. The play is set in and around a palace, so use whatever you have in the hall or garden to suggest grandeur – such as ornate pillars, large doorways, plush curtains, or even rhododendron bushes in flower! If you are performing indoors in a space which is shared with other activities like PE or school lunch, *The Willow Pattern* is a good play to select as you won't need an elaborate set that takes time to dismantle after each rehearsal or performance. The play could most simply be acted within a large circle of chairs or cushions for the audience to sit on.

Make sure that wherever you seat your audience they all have a clear view of the stage. If your stage is on the floor of the hall, it may be helpful to raise the audience's seating area, particularly the back rows, using some blocks, so that the audience is encouraged to focus on the action on-stage at all times – it's easy for an audience to lose concentration if they can't see properly.

It's likely that, most of the time, you won't be rehearsing the play in the space where you will perform it. So that you are aware of the dimensions of the space and the set, it's a good idea to mark on the rehearsal room floor an exact ground-plan of the performing space. You could do this with coloured PVC tape or masking tape, which your art department should be able to provide. If you are going to have any furniture or blocks in the production, mark where these are placed so that they are in exactly the same position each time you rehearse.

The design of *The Willow Pattern* does not have to be faithful to the famous images on the dinner plates. As Judith Johnson says in her introduction to the play, it doesn't even have to suggest the ancient Chinese myth upon which it is based; indeed, you could decide to set it in another culture entirely. However, if you do wish to use the blue and white colours found on the dinner service, they can be quite useful for establishing a basic set and costume design which can then be added to as each scene unfolds. For instance, if the audience is predominantly looking at a stage that is washed with pale blue, you could use large splashes of orange in the fire sequence for a striking visual effect. You should select a style and follow it through so that set, props and costumes all belong to the same 'world'. This is helpful in creating a strong and believable setting for the Mandarin's Palace and, therefore, helpful in telling the story. The play has collossal energy: this should be reflected and heightened through the design so that whilst your staging may be beautiful, it is also important to employ strong imagery and colour rather than too much detail and subtlety. If you look at the Narrator's opening speech, it's clear that the playwright's intention is to keep the audience intrigued and involved from the start. Strong images which join forces with the lively text will work well in achieving this style of storytelling.

PROPS

Think carefully about scene changes. This play works well without blackouts. Use all the actors as inventively as you can to change the locations right in front of the audience as this can be extremely magical. Blackouts, or a radical change of lighting, are useful for marking passages of time, and can give the audience breathing space after a long scene. Whatever you use in the way of props and furniture, make sure they are light enough for the actors to carry on and off the acting space so that they become part of the unfolding drama.

Photo: Simon Annand

All Saints College, Newcastle. Cottesloe Theatre, July 2004

There are many ways of achieving the effect of the two doves, which are very involved in the action. They might be two actors who are good dancers, who can suggest the movement of the birds with their whole bodies. They might be paper birds suspended by fishing line from bamboo canes carried around the stage by two actors dressed neutrally or in white. Or you might decide to have the doves played by the hands of the actors who happen to be on-stage in the scene when the doves are required. When they fly around the stage, the doves could be 'passed' from one actor to the next in a similar way to a Mexican wave. Look at the photograph above to see how All Saints College staged the doves. When Knoon-She holds them, the doves could be her own hands. Experiment with different ways of staging the birds and choose the one you think works best.

The fence is something that the actors could create using only their bodies. This way it is instant and can be any shape you wish. The actors could also use sticks and ropes that complement the style and colours used in the set, thus unifying them as 'the fence' at that moment.

Creating a convincing fire is not as difficult as you may think. For example, you could use lots of orange and red lighting. Or you might keep the colours on the stage cold and neutral up to the section which requires the fire, and then bring on lots of orange ribbons or strips of material and have the actors move them continuously to create the illusion of engulfing flames. This should be accompanied by a sound effect – either a realistic sound recording of fire, or a soundscape of fire created by actors slowly crackling noisy plastic sheets. The stream could be created in a similar way using lots of different shades of blue fabric and accompanying it with sounds made by rainsticks, or soft plastic being rustled to sound like running water. However, you will need to solve the problem of how to show the boat sailing along the stream with the bead in.

There is a real opportunity in *The Willow Pattern* to use shadow puppets to tell the story at certain moments when action sequences are required. This is an area you could explore, perhaps in collaboration with your art department. There is an informative weblink at www.osv.org/kids/crafts2.htm which explains how to make and use shadow puppets.

COSTUMES

The costumes you choose should immediately suggest another world. Whichever culture you set the play in, it should clear from the start that it is different to the world we live in. As soon as you have created a credible magical environment, the audience will find it easier to believe the magic that occurs within it. This leads to the most magical event in the story – the transformation from human being into bird, found on page 52.

You may decide that everyone in the company should wear a basic outfit that can be added to at certain times to denote particular characters. For example, the warriors could wear armour or carry shields. However, be imaginative about what the basic costume is. Plain T-shirts are very cheap and can be transformed using fabric pens – perhaps to reflect the characters' personalities in the costumes. For example, Ta-jin's Mother could be extravagantly overdressed when she visits the palace to see the Mandarin to present her son. Min could wear a dress which suggests that she is a little vulgar at times. Also, as Min is often seen working or washing clothes, she could wear a large apron with pockets to carry necessary hand-props. Similarly, as Chang is always writing poetry, he could wear a waistcoat or jacket so that he has somewhere to store his parchment and quill when he is not holding them. The whole company could then wear colourful hats or similar for the wedding celebration, while Knoon-She's wedding gown is an opportunity to go to town! Look for pieces of beautiful, ornate fabric and decide how the two handmaids will dress her with them. You could also give her fine jewellery and flowers. This is a wordless section of the play and should be carried out as an important ritual: the dressing of the bride at an arranged marriage.

All costumes should be kept simple so that costume changes don't hold up the pace of the action. One cleverly-chosen, unfussy garment will be more effective than those with lots of detail.

LIGHTING

It is quite possible to perform this play in bright daylight, without any focused electric lighting. If you are indoors, though, you may choose to light the whole play with the same lighting state. This could work well as the audience's imagination will be fired by the shapes and sounds the actors make, taking them from one time of day to another.

If you have a sophisticated lighting system at your disposal, you may choose to use rotating gobos to achieve the effects of the fire and the stream. (A gobo is a metal disc with an image cut into it, which is projected onto the stage floor or the scenery by a lantern, usually called a profile or sil. Rotating gobos give the effect of light moving and could be useful when creating flames and running water.) If only one narrator is used in the play, there is the opportunity to use a follow-spot on this actor, using a slightly different coloured gel to set this character apart from the story being enacted by the other actors. (A follow-spot is a very bright focused light on a stand, usually situated behind the audience, with a dedicated operator who follows the actor they are lighting through the performance.)

For the eve of the wedding scene, you may wish to suggest night-time by using very deep blue and purple gels on the general wash of lighting, and having paper lanterns with golden coloured lights inside them on-stage. Perhaps a romantic moon could gaze down upon the festivities to help to create a warm and friendly atmosphere on-stage, which can then be disrupted by the lovers' escape.

For the chase, you may have the facility on your lighting board to program a chase sequence using several lights. This would inject further energy into any action that the actors are creating on-stage.

There is huge potential with this play for a group of musicians to create a score which accompanies action throughout. Explore the styles of Peking Opera, Kabuki and Noh theatre to see how this works, and provide a variety of percussive instruments. If a small group of musicians join in rehearsals, the music will grow with the acting. Their instruments will serve to create atmosphere, which helps establish the location of each scene, and they can be used to mark important moments of action, for example rejection, a grand entrance, Chang's sadness or the Mandarin's anger. The musicians could also perform in the play, as guests at the wedding celebration and as musicians at the funeral at the end.

You may also want to use realistic sound effects for moments like the fire, and sound effects CDs are available from large music stores.

Information

Peking Opera is a combination of stylised action, singing, dialogue and mime, acrobatic fighting and dancing to represent a story or depict different characters and their emotions.

Kabuki is a traditional form of Japanese theatre. It was founded early in the 17th century. Kabuki plays can be about anything from grand historical events to everyday life.

Noh is a classical Japanese performance form which combines elements of dance, drama, music and poetry into a highly intense ritualistic stage art.

Improvising music

As an experiment, gather together all the percussive instruments you can find (such as drums, cymbals, bells) and also any junk that you think makes an interesting sound. Sit in a large circle and invite the actors to underline the story by improvising with the sounds as you do a full reading of the play.

Note in your scripts all the instinctive moments when the group thought collectively that music was required to heighten the drama.

Work on and around the script

Allow plenty of time to rehearse *The Willow Pattern*. Since the play isn't split up into scenes, it would be helpful to divide it into units of about six or eight pages so that you can write a rehearsal schedule. You might like to break the play into units and give each one a name, for example 'Wedding'. A unit may also begin and end with the arrival or exit of a main character.

Dividing the play into units

It can be revealing to carry out the following task to help you get an overall view of the play's structure.

- Photocopy the play so that each page occupies a full page of A4.

- Divide the play into units, and give each unit a title that refers to the main action that happens within the unit.

- Sticky tape each unit together into a long continuous strip, and write the title of the unit in bold at the top of each strip of paper.

- Hang the units on a wall in order from left to right: from the start of the play to the end.

You will then have a strong visual representation of how the play works structurally, and it will also help in your planning of rehearsal time.

Make sure that you stick to the schedule so that you don't run out of time to rehearse the end of the play. If people are absent from rehearsals, have someone else stand-in for them and take notes of what their character is doing – this makes it easier for that actor to catch up at the next rehearsal. Spend plenty of time rehearsing each scene, avoiding jumping from one to another. If you work in this way you will thoroughly rehearse each scene, and the actors will be able to get a good grasp of their lines whilst learning the moves. Remember, it is nearly always easier to learn lines within the context of action.

It is important that, as you learn the play, you are accurate in the way you learn the lines. Judith Johnson has thought very carefully

59

about every word in her play and it is important that you don't change anything. You may choose which actors are to play which parts during the first few rehearsals, which should be experimental sessions where everyone has fun exploring the possibilities of staging. People could have the opportunity to try out various roles. By the third or fourth rehearsal, you should confirm the casting. If you find some of the casting is not working out, change parts around to solve the problems.

Getting to know the story

Using the units you have stuck to the wall, divide the whole drama class into small groups.

Give each group one unit each and tell them they have only three minutes to rehearse that unit. They should work away from the script and make up the lines themselves, on the understanding that it must be clear who is who, where the scene takes place, and what the main action in the scene is.

As soon as the period of rapid improvisation is over, perform the units in order.

Getting to know the plot

You can then try an exercise in which you ask each group to perform the entire play in one minute – which is not as impossible as it may sound. They must include all the crucial units in some way and be as specific as possible.

When the work is shared, it will be interesting to see the different choices made by each group, for instance where they have placed focus and emphasis.

Sit back down in a circle and discuss the choices that emerge from the exercise.

You should start by reading through the script carefully and slowly. Involve absolutely everyone who will take part in the production – including those who will be selling the tickets so that they have a good understanding of what the play is about and will be able to talk about it to audience members who may phone the school to book tickets.

During the read-through, actors should hold their scripts so that they can project the lines out into the circle and make eye contact with the characters to whom they are speaking. If they are having private, spoken thoughts, they can deliver them to the middle-distance – the area in the middle of the circle – with no eye contact. If the lines are delivered to the audience, they should try to make contact with as many of the rest of the cast as possible. Encourage the actors to ask questions if there are words or lines they don't understand. This kind of detailed work will really pay off when you start to work on your feet.

CHARACTERS

All the main characters in *The Willow Pattern* undergo changes during the play. Encourage the main actors to have a small area of the drama studio or classroom that they dedicate to that character for the duration of the rehearsal period. Suggest that they collect photos, pictures and objects from today's world which they think tell the history of that character to date. If they were playing the Mandarin, for example, they could collect photos from magazines of other important leaders in the world; if playing Ta-Jin they could collect things they think he may play with if he was alive and living in this world.

Encourage the actors to add to these collections each time they make a discovery about their character. Other members of the group may wish to contribute objects too, but these should only be added with the agreement of the actor interpreting that particular role.

Diary: writing in character

Set all the actors the task of writing a diary of the life of one of the characters for one year up to the point where the play begins. If there are gaps in what you know about the characters' histories, encourage the actors to invent facts accordingly. They could draw pictures to illustrate important events in their lives or of people they have met.

Discussion of characters

Ask each of the main actors to lie down on a large sheet of paper and invite somebody else to draw round them with a felt-tip marker. Pin the sheets on the wall and clearly mark each one with the name of that character.

cont...

Invite the whole cast to suggest what the rest of the people in the play think about that character, and write all the words around the character's outline. Inside the outline, ask the actor who is playing that character to write down what they believe that character thinks and feels internally.

When finished, sit back and take a good look at each character's display. Discuss each one in turn. Are there any contrasting words on the inside and outside of each character? Discuss how these contradictions occur within the context of the story.

Status through drama

Everyone should take it in turns to play the Mandarin, with the whole class improvising scenes from everyday life off-script. Point out that the Mandarin is a very important man. Encourage the class to think of a famous leader, e.g. the Prime Minister or a member of the royal family, and each to take turns to act in a way that shows great authority and power. The rest of the company should show as low status as possible when around the Mandarin and do whatever he commands. Give everyone the chance each to play the Mandarin for one to two minutes.

When the exercise is finished, discuss who achieved the strongest status and how they showed it. Was it in the way they moved? The way they spoke to their subjects?

Exploring character through movement

Ask everyone to start walking around your rehearsal space. Encourage them to follow their own journey and not to make eye contact with anyone else. They should find as neutral a walk as possible and relax through the body.

When this is achieved, call out the names of the main characters one at a time. As each character's name is called, everyone should assume the walk and physical actions of that character as they imagine them. When everyone is walking in character, count down from ten to zero and ask everyone to freeze as a statue of that character.

You may wish to split the group in half at this point so that everyone has a chance to be in character and to walk around them as if at a sculpture exhibition.

Repeat this for each character.

Action in character: entrances

Set up a clearly defined entrance to your acting space. Ask each actor, in turn, to choose a character and to walk through the entrance in character. Everyone else should try to guess which character they have chosen. You may wish to extend this by having each character enter, look around and then sit down on a chair.

Drama discussion: strong and weak places on-stage

Divide the group into two halves. Have one half sit as the audience and the other half experiment with standing, sitting or lying in various places on your acting space.

Discuss which parts of the space are strong and weak from an audience's point of view. How can the weak and strong places be useful in the way that you stage the play to tell the story? Discuss how different people seem to connect or appear isolated, depending on where they are placed on the stage.

Poetry: writing in character

Everyone in the class should imagine that they are Chang and read the poem in the play aloud. Then imagine other poetry that Chang would write to Knoon-She. Write one of these poems.

You may want to write it on parchment paper in special handwriting, decorating the text with images as you write.

 ENSEMBLE WORK

The Willow Pattern has endless opportunities for physical theatre to be carried out by the ensemble of actors, who can be of any age (or age ranges) and experience. Begin sessions that focus on ensemble work with a thorough warm-up exercise that loosens all the joints in the body and frees the actors from thinking about the text and being self-conscious.

Ask the actors find a good space in the room. Prompt them to stretch through their bodies and relax, repeating several times. Alternate this stretching and relaxing with rapid exercise such as jumping or hopping around the room. This serves to warm up the bodies physically and stretches any muscles avoiding strains and tensions.

The actors must then find focus as a group. It is very important when working as a large group with the same goal that everyone is contributing to the creative process with the same energy.

Group focus

A good exercise to do here is to ask everyone to stand in a circle and hold hands. The leader then sends a pulse, which is a slight squeeze of the hand they are holding, to the person standing next to them. This pulse is invisible. It should be passed on all the way around the circle so that it arrives back at the leader. The group should concentrate totally on the sense of touch for this exercise. They should not giggle; they should not allow anyone to see them passing on the pulse. (Note: It can be helpful to ask everyone to close their eyes to increase concentration on touch.)

Once the pulse has been round the circle a few times, the leader can time how long it takes by counting seconds aloud. The aim is to try and send the pulse around the circuit of hands as quickly as possible, so that it zips along like electricity. Once the group are good at doing that, the leader can start a pulse off and then introduce another one going in the opposite direction around the circle. This makes the group work together with intense focus, and they become very alert as they could receive a pulse at any moment in either hand and must respond to it instantly.

Physical warm-up

Another exercise which will motivate the group to work together physically is to have them walk slowly around the room. The leader then shouts out two numbers: the first is the number of people they should get themselves into groups of; and the second is the number of points of contact they may have with the floor. Encourage the actors to be inventive in the shapes they create. So, for example, for a group of 30 actors, the leader could shout out "5 and 3!" Everyone would then have to rush into groups of five and work out a way of having only three points of contact with the floor. The first group to achieve this is the winner. Repeat the exercise several times, being more ambitious each time. Another benefit of doing this exercise is that the actors will break any barriers they have about having physical contact with each other: when the game is played fast, there is no time to think or have inhibitions.

When the group is ready to start experimenting with ways to create the physical objects needed to tell the story, it might be useful to look at pictures or photos of fences, palaces and banquets for visual ideas. The actors should then work instinctively to create the objects and arrive at a solution for each one. They should add as much detail as possible to each creation – and also be very tidy in the execution of each physical shape.

Once the group has become familiar with working physically to create the different landscapes and architecture needed to tell the story, they can begin to experiment with finding ways of 'morphing' from one shape to another. A good way to do this is to have somebody slowly beat a low-pitched drum and count from one to ten whilst the actors change their shape from a bridge to a fence, for example. Be as inventive as you can in the rehearsal room, and keep adding detail to your physical creations. You will find that you discover some magical ways of changing scene, which can be as interesting to watch as the rest of the play itself.

You will also find that extensive work on developing the physical work of the ensemble will give you ideas of how to add extra atmosphere to other scenes. For example, you might discover how to create tension at the end of the wedding scene by prompting the crowd of wedding guests to react to the tension generated by what happens to the main characters. The Mandarin's temper should be reflected by his subjects in both their faces and bodies. Dramatic effect can often be achieved by a crowd suddenly becoming silent.

The Narrator as Chorus

In Greek drama, a chorus of actors who were not playing named parts would comment on the story between scenes. It is possible in this play to interpret the character of the Narrator as a chorus group. Therefore, experiment with the speech on page 66 to see if you like this approach and if it could work well in your production.

You should work slowly in small groups and take a few lines at a time. Make decisions about who says each line, and whether they're spoken by solo voices or by everyone. You will need to decide which words need to be stressed.

You may also think it would be effective for some of the Chorus to speak echoes of certain words, or to take vowel or consonant sounds and sustain them to create atmosphere. Decide when pauses could be important. Experiment with giving the speech using different speeds and levels of volume.

cont...

> You should also think about how the Chorus could move as a whole group to illustrate the speech. Try to think of movement which shows the emotions in the speech rather than the action words which are used.

What sadness! What sorrow and sadness and strain. The Mandarin was so angry with his daughter, he placed a high fence round the Palace and Garden, and refused to let her see anyone! He sent out warriors, searching for Chang high and low, promising a reward of four donkeys to anyone who could bring back his dead body. And worse of all, he told Knoon-She he had decided something. He had decided she was to marry Ta-Jin after all. Knoon-She was heartbroken. She wandered the garden day after day, thinking about Chang. She wouldn't admit it to herself, but deep in her heart she felt he was dead.

Not even her old maid Min had been allowed to see her, so there was no one to tell her that Chang had not been found, and no one knew where he was. She was more unhappy then she had ever been in her life but, as it is said, 'The soul would have no rainbow if the eyes had no tears.'

MARTIAL ARTS

The actor playing Ta-Jin will have to learn at least six different martial arts moves for the scene where he demonstrates his skills. Ideally you should try to find someone around your school who attends judo or karate lessons, who is able to come in for a lesson and teach some basic moves. It may be sensible to borrow a mat from the PE department when you are learning these physical skills. It may also be useful for the whole company to learn the moves, as you could incorporate them later in the play during the chase section or when the Mandarin first calls for his warriors. A useful weblink can be found at: http://martialarts.about.com.

Monkey is based on the 16th-century Chinese story *Hsi Yu Chi (Journey to the West)*. It tells the story of the Buddhist priest Tripitaka and his three disciples, Monkey, Pigsy and Sandy, as they travel from China to India to fetch the Buddhist scriptures. They have been sent by Buddha, and getting these scriptures will bring peace to the people of the world. On this journey they must face many dangers and challenges. All the characters have very distinctive personalities: Monkey is a brave fighter, who has magical powers, and is very mischievous; Pigsy is less brave, and has a weakness for food and women; Sandy is the thinker, and much more a thinker than a doer; Tripitaka is a sometimes naive young man, who trusts everyone and is unaware of the evils of the world.

While the subject matter sounds serious, and although there is a religious theme, the show contains lots of humour – often highlighting the clash in personalities between the main characters.

Visit the website www.monkeyheaven.com and learn all about one of Judith Johnson's key inspirations when she was writing *The Willow Pattern*. You will get a good idea of the energy Judith imagines performances of *The Willow Pattern* will have.

A scene from Monkey

From legend to contemporary play

The story of the Willow Pattern

Knoon-She, daughter of the Mandarin, is in love with her father's secretary, Chang, but has been ordered by her parents to wed a wealthy rival suitor.

She refuses to comply with his wishes, whereupon her enraged father locks her up from where she successfully sends a message to her lover. Thus encouraged, Chang succeeds in entering the apple orchard and escaping with his beloved.

They hurry over the bridge, Chang carrying Knoon-She's box of jewels, pursued by the angry Mandarin brandishing a whip.

The lovers make good their escape in a ship, landing on an island where they take refuge in a little wooden house. But the father and discarded suitor find their hideaway and set fire to the house while they are sleeping and the lovers perish.

Next morning Knoon-She's and Chang's spirits rise, phoenix-like, in the form of two doves with outstretched wings, flying off to the realms of eternal happiness.

Judith Johnson freely adapted the legend of the Willow Pattern to write her play. You should find that all of the elements of the story above are contained in Judith's play.

Discussion

What has Judith added to the play to make it feel timeless?

How has she created characters which can be understood in any age or culture?

Which scenes in the play remind you of events which have happened in your own life?

What if Knoon-She's mother was a character in the play. Her mother dies, which adds to her father's grief. How is he affected by the loss?

Themes in and around the play

 ARRANGED MARRIAGES

Read the three extracts below on the theme of arranged marriages. They may be helpful when you come to debate the pros and cons.

> Punjabi parents desire beautiful, professional, never married, US-raised girl for handsome son, 34, 5'10"/150, fair, slim, athletic, engineer/MBA, consultant in DC area. Enjoys travel, sports, music. Please reply...

(Source: an advert placed in American Press, June 2004)

"Although Western societies tend to deride arranged marriages as backward and uncivilized and primitive, there do exist positive aspects. For example, Westerners focus more on the physical aspect of relationships, and are thus obsessed with love, sex, beauty, etc. As a result, people get married based on these factors and then get disenchanted with one another very easily. The divorce rate in Western countries such as the US has skyrocketed. In contrast, Eastern cultures that practice arranged marriages place far more emphasis on the practical, such as integrity, diligence, ambition, humility, generosity, etc. People get married based on practical reasons, and work on building affection later. Strong characteristics like the ones described above are very conducive to building love and affection in Eastern marriages. As a result, these marriages are much longer-lasting than many Western marriages. It's BECAUSE the primary emphasis is NOT on love, sex, and physical beauty that arranged marriages are usually so successful, because the spouses get to know one another on a practical level first, looking beyond trivial issues such as beauty or lack thereof."

Another contributor to this online discussion board had this comment:

"But are divorce rates really a measure of successful marriage? Do all the couples that don't get divorced stay happy with each other? The prevalence of divorce in a society depends on a lot of factors including the stigma of divorce."

Debate

As a way of exploring one of the central themes in The Willow Pattern organise a session of Forum Theatre with the cast of your play. Forum Theatre is the type of performance where the audience are invited to join in a discussion which is started off by actors 'in-role' giving opposing points of view. It is similar to a debate. The audience do not necessarily have to give their own views — you could organise it so that all points of view are covered and all members of the forum speak in-role.

There is a generally a lack of understanding and support in the Western world for arranged marriages. They haven't been a part of our culture for many centuries, except in the aristocracy. You should use the Forum Theatre exercise to try and discover why this is, and use internet search engines extensively to find out about the many cultures and places in the world where arranged marriages are common practice.

Comparing texts – Romeo and Juliet

Read the following extract from William Shakespeare's play about forbidden love. What similarities can you see between Romeo and Juliet and Chang and Knoon-She?

Act 2, Scene Two

JULIET My ears have not yet drunk a hundred words
Of that tongue's utterance,[1] yet I know the sound:
Art thou not Romeo and a Montague?

ROMEO Neither, fair saint, if either thee dislike.

JULIET How camest thou hither, tell me, and wherefore?
The orchard walls are high and hard to climb,
And the place death, considering who thou art,
If any of my kinsmen[2] find thee here.

ROMEO With love's light wings did I o'er-perch[3] these walls;
For stony limits cannot hold love out,
And what love can do that dares love attempt;
Therefore thy kinsmen are no let to me.

JULIET If they do see thee, they will murder thee.

ROMEO Alack,[4] there lies more peril in thine eye
Than twenty of their swords: look thou but sweet,
And I am proof against their enmity.[5]

JULIET I would not for the world they saw thee here.

ROMEO I have night's cloak to hide me from their sight;
And but thou love me, let them find me here:
My life were better ended by their hate,
Than death prorogued,[6] wanting of thy love.

Glossary	[1] utterance – speech	[3] o'er-perch – fly over	[5] enmity – hate
	[2] kinsmen – family	[4] Alack – regretfully	[6] prorogued – deferred

Willow Pattern poem (*anon*)

Two little birdies flying high
a little vessel passing by
a weeping willow hanging o'er
a bridge with three men, if not four.
a Chinese castle there it stands
as if the Lord of many lands,
a tree with many apples on,
and a fence at the bottom to end my song.

Two big birds flying high
a little ship, passing by
three men standing on the shore,
a willow tree hanging o'er
an idle temple, there it stands
it wasn't built without hands,
an orange tree with oranges on,
and iron railings right along.

Two pigeons flying high
sailing vessel passing by,
a bridge with three and not with four.
a weeping willow hanging o'er,
Chinese castle here it stands,
apple tree with apples on,
and a zig zag fence below
which ends my song.

Two birds flying high,
Little boat passing by.
Wooden bridge with willow o'er
Three men passing, if not four,
A little house with open door
Apple tree with apples on,
Iron railings all around
To keep the boys away.

Two doves flying high,
Chinese vessel sailing by,
Weeping willow hanging o'er
Bridge with three men, and not with four,
Chinese teahouse there it stands
Seems to take up all the land,
Orange tree with fruit thereon,
A pretty fence to end my song.

Writing

In pairs, read through the sayings below and discuss times in your own lives when you know that they have been true.

Still working in pairs, now invent your own sayings. Write them on small pieces of card and hang them on your own piece of willow tree in your theatre entrance or classroom. It may be fun to try and guess which cast members wrote which sayings!

'He that is angry is seldom at ease'   *Unknown origin*

'A friend is one who knows everything about you, and yet still likes you'
                                                              Unknown origin

'He who wears his heart on his sleeve, often looks stupid'.
                                                              Judith Johnson

'To get used to something is something terrible'   *Zen master*

'Happiness is like a perfume, we can not sprinkle it on someone else, without a few drops falling on ourselves.'
                                                        William Shakespeare

'Love, and a cough, cannot be hid'.   *George Herbert*

'The soul would have no rainbow if the eyes had no tears'
                                                            Indian Proverb

'All roads lead you astray'   *Lonely Planet Guide Book*

'If we do not change direction, we will probably get to where we are going'
                                                            Chinese adage

'I have my ignorance to thank for the few things I know'
                                                            Sacha Guitry

'You have only failed when you have failed to try'.
                                                            Unknown origin

'You can get everything you want in life, if you help enough other people get what they want'.
                                                            Unknown origin

'Those who think of revenge keep their wounds open'
                                                            Francis Bacon

Icebreaker: fun improvisation

This could be used to distract your cast from any first-night nerves they may have!

Everyone in the cast should imagine that they are one of the donkeys in Willow Pattern world. Waiting in their stable, they should decide what sort of a donkey they are and what their views are of the human characters in the play. They should then quickly improvise a scene in which they discuss how they feel about donkeys being used as currency or as forms of bribery and bartering.

If the donkeys agree with something that one of the donkeys says, they should all make a loud braying sound: "Eeeee!" If the donkeys find they disagree with something that is being said, they should make a long protesting sound "Awwwww!"

Transformation: writing assignment

The Willow Pattern ends with a transformation scene in which Knoon-She and Chang become the two doves of the story.

Read the story of The Beauty and the Beast. Discuss how the ending becomes a happy one when the Beast is transformed into a handsome prince. What is the effect of a happy ending through transformation?

Ask your cast members what they think they would be transformed into if such magic occurred in their lives. Why do you think transformations take place in stories? Create your own story in which there is a transformation scene.

ACTIVITIES MAPPING

English Framework Objectives (Year 7/8/9)

Page Number	Word (W) & Sentence (S) Level	Learning Objectives (Year 7/8/9)		Speaking & Listening
		Text Level		
		Reading	Writing	
59		(7) 17, 18 (8) 5, 10 (9) 14		
60				(7) 16, 19 (8) 12, 13, 16 (9) 12, 14
61	(7) 13	(7) 17, 18		
62		(7) 17, 18		(7) 17 (8) 10, 15, 16 (9) 12
63			(7) 9 (8) 9 (9) 8	
67		(7) 1		
70		(8) 5		(7) 1, 3 (8) 15, 16 (9) 12

National Theatre Workshops are available to support your work on this play.

There are two options available for you:

Visit the National Theatre on London's Southbank to attend a teachers' one-day INSET on the play facilitated by a director and the writer of the play. These INSET days are programmed regularly throughout the academic year and a limited number of places are available.

Host a one-day workshop at your school led by a National Theatre director and the author of the play. The day will be spent working with your staff and students on the text of this play.

For further information on prices, booking a workshop, and forthcoming dates of INSETs please contact Connections Enterprises on 0207 452 3728.

You can also:

Participate in the current Connections Programme and have access to the newest set of plays. See the Connections website for details.

For information on all the workshops and other projects about new writing for young people offered by Connections Enterprises for your school visit:

www.nationaltheatre.org.uk/connections/enterprises

The Exam
Andy Hamilton

Collins

the exam
andy hamilton

National
Theatre

The Exam is a comic look at the pressures put on young people by parents and teachers.

Andrew, Chas and Bea are three candidates of mixed ability who find themselves holed up in the same exam hall waiting for their papers to arrive.

As the wait lengthens, each has to survive a powerful barrage of self-doubt, parental pressure and adult incompetence. They must come to terms with themselves, their peers and parents – provoked and helped by 'Ex', the mysterious, disembodied voice of the exam.

Mugged

Andrew Payne

Every morning a group of teenagers meet up on their way to school and hang out on the benches in the park. And every morning they are faced with the same dilemma: take the short cut across the park to school and risk running into the muggers, or go the long way around and risk being late.

When Soph has her phone stolen, Marky thinks he recognises one of the muggers and volunteers to retrieve it for her. But it goes horribly wrong...